Happy, Healthy George!

Written by Jessica Wollman

Houghton Mifflin Harcourt
Boston   New York

George is a curious little monkey.
He is also a healthy monkey!

George likes to exercise.
He likes to stretch and move.
Exercise helps him stay
healthy.

George likes to play ball.
He likes to run and jump
and throw.

George likes to play jump rope, too.
He moves his legs and swings his arms.

It's snack time!
George eats a healthy snack.
Healthy food helps George
move and grow and think.

Now it's time to rest.
Sleep helps George's body grow.
It helps his brain grow too!

Rest time is over.
What will George do now?

It is time for a dance party!
Dancing is good exercise.
And so much fun!